Contents

First published 2014 by Brown Watson
The Old Mill, 76 Fleckney Road
Kibworth Beauchamp
Leicestershire LE8 0HG

ISBN: 978 0 7097 2183 3

Bella has long, floppy ears and a very twitchy nose. She loves to get cuddles from Michael. Billy is not a cuddly bunny. He doesn't want cuddles – he just wants to run!

Naughty Billy doesn't stay in the hutch when their owner comes to clean it. He always makes a break for freedom and dashes off. 'There he goes again!' sighs Michael. 'What are we going to do with him?'

Bella has an idea. She picks up a carrot and hops into the garden. She places the carrot on the path and then goes back for another. Soon, there is a line of carrots leading all the way to their hutch.

Billy races past and then sees the first carrot. He stops and sniffs, and follows the trail. 'Welcome back, Billy!' says Bella. Billy likes to run, but he LOVES to eat!

Did you see these things?

Lettuce

Ladybird

Shed

Rabbit food

Brush

Straw

Playing Together

Steggy and Tricky are going out to play. They love to play football in the forest clearing. 'Can we come too?' ask their friends, who also love football.

'Sorry, only two players allowed,' says Steggy. 'Otherwise it's no fun.' Steggy is in a mean mood and doesn't want to play nicely. He kicks the ball to Tricky, who dribbles it in front of him.

The two friends tackle each other and take turns to play in goal and take penalties. Then Steggy kicks the ball really hard and it disappears over the treetops.

The little dinosaurs hunt for ages, but they can't find their ball. They sit on a rock and get very bored and grumpy. Then Dippy trundles past. 'Aren't you playing any more?' he asks. Tricky explains what has happened.

'Tee hee, that's bad luck,' says Dippy, and calls for his friends. He climbs up on their backs and stretches his long neck upwards. 'I can see it!' he calls, and races off to collect the lost ball.

Tricky and Steggy shout to him. 'That's our ball! Bring it back!' But Dippy replies, 'Finders keepers!' He and his other friends all play nicely together, and hope that Tricky and Steggy will learn their lesson.

Read these words again

tackle	dribbles
forest	upwards
collect	penalties
football	disappears
clearing	allowed
players	dinosaurs
nicely	stretches

Did you see these things?

Purple plant

Ball

T-rex

Horn

Flying reptiles

Sky Spotting

Tim lives on a farm with his mum and his dad. He helps whenever he can. Today he is feeding the hens. He loves to watch them peck around at the grains of corn scattered on the ground.

As Tim listens to their gentle clucking noises, he gazes at the clouds floating past in the blue sky. 'Look!' he shouts out loud. 'That cloud looks exactly like a tractor!'

The farm animals hear Tim, and they all look into the sky. Sally the sheep baas excitedly because she can see a cloud shaped like a woolly lamb. Raffles the dog barks, as she can see a bone.

Toffee, the gentle pony, spots a saddle-shaped cloud. Marmalade the cat thinks it sounds like a silly game, but sure enough, when she opens one eye she can see a cloud like a fish, floating high above her!

Raffles barks to wake Olly the owl in the old tree. 'Can you see what we can see?' he asks. Olly peeps out from his resting place. 'I do believe I can see clouds like white mice!' he agrees.

Olly settles back down to sleep. He knows that everyone can see shapes in the clouds, if they only try. Isn't it funny how they each see something that is special to them?

Read these words again

gazes	special
saddle	woolly
gentle	shaped
listens	enough
clouds	floating
feeding	whenever
resting	excitedly

Did you see these things?

Sheepdog

Chick

Dandelion

Flower

Whiskers

Brown hen

A Helping Hand

Once upon a time, in a palace far, far away, there lived a princess. She was called Avaline and she was a very good girl.

Avaline had no brothers or sisters, but she did have lots of servants. She had servants to do her hair, choose her clothes, get her dressed, clean her teeth, and even read to her. The problem was, this left nothing for her to do. She was bored.

Princess Avaline often wandered around the palace, asking if she could help anyone. She tried to help in the kitchen, but they sent her away. She wanted to help in the garden, but they wouldn't let her do anything.

Eventually, Avaline went into the stables to see if she could help there. The stable girls just laughed. 'You can't help in these dirty stables! You are wearing fine clothes and a crown!'

The poor princess didn't care about her clothes. She just wanted something to do. Then one of the stable girls tugged her sleeve. 'Here, miss,' she said. 'You can have these old clothes.'

Avaline quickly got changed and was soon mucking out the horses. She was so happy! Now she helps every day, and the stable girls have time to play with the princess in her royal bedroom, too.

Did you see these things?

Book

Crown

Bucket

Tower

Brush

Broom

On the Run

Rufus is a scruffy, lovable puppy. He loves to play and can often be found racing around, chasing his own tail. He usually dashes around the farmyard looking for other animals to join in his games.

Today, though, Rufus seems upset. He hasn't talked to anybody all morning, and isn't playing any of his usual games. He just runs from place to place, peeping into buildings and behind vehicles.

The white farm mice run
around after Rufus and
wonder what he is doing.
They watch in astonishment as
he bounds onto his basket and
grabs his cushion between
his teeth.

Rufus shakes his cushion from
side to side, and then does
the same with his blanket. His
food bowl flies up into the air
and dog biscuits scatter across
the floor. What a mess!

'Rufus, what on earth is wrong?' squeaks Mummy Mouse eventually. Rufus explains that he can't find his favourite blue bone anywhere. He looks ever so sad.

'Well, why didn't you say?' smiles Mummy Mouse. 'I saw it just a while ago. It is hidden under the bright rug, in front of the fireplace.' Rufus dashes across and finds it. Now he is a happy pup again!

Read these words again

upset	lovable
hidden	blanket
morning	buildings
basket	vehicles
chasing	wonder
dashes	cushion
anybody	biscuits

The other patients don't like it when Alfonso is around. 'I do wish he'd be quiet,' growls Lenny the lion. 'Yes,' agrees Teddy the tiger, 'he's so loud we can hear him coming up the corridor.'

Sergio the snake hisses and hides under the covers. 'Ooooh, I feel sssssssssick,' he moans. 'Make that sssssilly frog go away.' What a grumpy bunch they are!

Luckily for the animals, Alfonso has a very kind heart. After his check up, he takes the time to visit each one of them and ask how they are. He makes sure they are comfortable, and tells funny stories to cheer them up.

Soon, the animals are smiling and laughing. They are glad he has a loud voice so they can all hear what he has to say. Now they can't wait for his next visit!

Read these words again

grumpy

visit

greets

booming

voice

hospital

patients

stories

quiet

luckily

comfortable

smiling

laughing

corridor

Did you see these things?

Nurse's hat

Tiger

Sick snake

Wheelchair

Medical chart

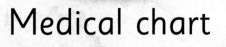

Poorly leg

The Ballet Show

Today is a very exciting day. Megan's ballet teacher has just told them that they are putting on a show. Megan and her friends are all very excited. 'Hurray!' they cheer, and join hands to dance around together.

The ballet teacher claps her hands for quiet. 'There will be auditions next week for all the main parts,' she explains. 'So please do lots of practice and try your very hardest.'

Megan's mum helps her to learn a new dance for the audition. Megan practises every day. She hopes that she will be chosen to play a dancing animal with a cute, furry costume.

The big day arrives and Megan puts on her best ballet dress. Her kitten watches as she ties the ribbons on her shoes, and then runs off to chase a butterfly through the bluebells in the garden.

Megan dances extremely well and is told she can be in the show. She is a little bit sad to find out that she won't be one of the animals. She cheers up when she sees her dress.

She is going to play a bluebell fairy, with a costume like the flowers in her own garden! 'This is going to be the best show EVER!' smiles Megan.

Read these words again

garden	hardest
chosen	together
flowers	exciting
arrives	teacher
quiet	audition
watches	butterfly
ribbons	costume

Did you see these things?

Rabbit ear

Bluebells

Bird mask

Mouse outfit

Spotty tights

Very Proud

Farmer Jim has a new, red tractor. It is shiny and smart and he is very proud of it. In fact, he doesn't stop talking about it. He tells everyone how good it is.

Gabby Goose is fed up of the tractor. 'He loves that lump of metal more than he loves us,' she moans. 'But it doesn't lay wonderful eggs like I do, does it?'

Farmer Jim drives his tractor around to show it off to the other animals. 'Well,' moos Connie Cow. 'It doesn't provide his whole family with milk, does it?'

'Indeed not!' crows Rocky Rooster. 'It is very colourful, but then so am I! And it doesn't wake him up in the mornings like I do!'

The animals don't want to hear about the new tractor. Farmer Jim realises that they aren't very happy. 'Oh, my lovelies!' he exclaims. 'You don't need to worry. I still love you all very much. It's only a piece of machinery, after all.'

The animals feel much happier after that. But it doesn't stop Farmer Jim admiring his tractor when the animals aren't around. Now his poor wife has to listen to him!

Read these words again

worry	wonderful
metal	mornings
listen	colourful
provide	realises
talking	machinery
tractor	happier
hearing	admiring

Did you see these things?

Cup of tea

Green hat

Goat

Tree

Tail feathers

Sausage

A Secret Surprise

Binky was a little white foal who lived in a forest. She was feeling sad and tried to explain to the others. 'I don't look like you do,' she neighed. 'I have bumps on my head and back, and I'm the only white one here.'

The ponies told her not to worry, and that they loved her no matter what she looked like. But Binky was still sad.

One wise old pony took Binky to one side. She told Binky that there was a reason she looked different, and that as she grew older she would find out why.

Sure enough, as the months passed, Binky's body started to change. The bump on her head got bigger, until it finally spiralled upwards as a horn. Wings sprouted from her back. She was a unicorn!

'It's time for you to leave us,' said the ponies. 'Your herd is waiting for you.' Sure enough, they were woken one day by the sound of beating wings. They looked up to see Binky's family coming to find her.

Binky took to the skies and joined her parents. They waved to the ponies on earth to say thank you, and then off they flew. Binky's adventures had just begun!

Read these words again

older	finally
matter	started
forest	waiting
family	woken
explain	different
feeling	adventures
reason	spiralled

Did you see these things?

Pink cloud

Bluebird

Worried
horse

Black
horse

Unicorn
horn

A Tricky Trick

Trixie is a little mouse who doesn't like going to school. She would much rather be playing out, or going swimming, or reading her book. School is too dull!

One day, Trixie decides to skip school. She stands in front of the mirror and carefully draws red spots all over her face and arms. Ooh, Trixie, that's naughty! You're bound to get caught!

When Trixie's mummy sees the spots, she calls for Grandma Mouse. 'Hmm, I've never seen anything like it,' she says. 'You'd better go back to bed.'

Trixie snuggles under the covers and reads her book for a while. 'Can I watch TV?' she shouts. 'I'm getting a little bit bored.' Grandma winks at Mummy Mouse. They both know that Trixie isn't really ill.

'Are your spots very itchy?'
asks Grandma. 'Maybe you'd
like to go for a swim?' Trixie is
very bored, so she thinks that's
a great idea and leaps
quickly out of bed.

Mummy and Grandma watch
as Trixie jumps in the river. She
has forgotten that her spots
aren't real, and they wash off
as soon as she is in the water.
Uh-oh Trixie! You've been
tricked! Off you go to school!

Read these words again

covers   reading

school   decides

bored   carefully

mouse   naughty

playing   caught

mirror   itchy

swimming   forgotten

Did you see these things?

Pink bow

Mouse house

Spider

Apron

Drink

Comic

A New Baby

This is Haidee Hadrosaur and her children. She has five new babies, but they are all waiting for the sixth egg to hatch and complete the family.

'Mama, mama, when will it come?' they all chirrup. They are excited and want to meet their brother or sister. Haidee tells them to be patient, but she can't wait either. She loves her babies so much!

Suddenly, a giant shadow looms over them and the babies all hide under their mother. It is one of the mean Apatosaurus brothers and everyone is scared of them.

The enormous dinosaur picks the last egg from the nest and kicks it into the air. 'Excellent – a rugby ball!' he laughs. He throws it to his brothers who join in the game. Haidee runs after them.

Haidee tries to grab the egg, but the brothers kick it high into the air out of her reach. It lands in the river with a splash. 'No!' she cries, as she can't swim.

Luckily, the egg floats up the river and is rescued by a kindly plesiosaur. She plops it back onto Haidee's nest. The egg cracks and a tiny head pops out and says 'Mama!' The other babies are delighted!

Read these words again

reach	throws
mother	patient
hatch	either
babies	shadow
splash	enormous
floats	rescued
complete	delighted

Did you see these things?

Egg shells

Volcano

Baby dinosaur

Purple tree

Flying reptile

93